That's Strange!

Compiled by Pat Edwards and Wendy Body

Did you hear what Dinosaur ?

Acknowledgements

We are grateful to the following for permission to reproduce copyright material: the author, Peg Dunstan for her poem 'Here Boy' (The Teradactyls have all gone); Penguin Books Ltd for the poems 'So Big' from p.14 *Songs For My Dog and Other People* by Max Fatchen (Kestrel Books, 1980) Copyright © 1980 by Max Fatchen and 'Fork Week' by Michael Rosen from pp.52-3 *You Tell Me* by Roger McGough and Michael Rosen (Kestrel Books, 1979) Copyright © Michael Rosen 1979; Viking Penguin Inc. for the story 'Cam Jansen and The Mystery of The Alligator Bones' by David A. Adler Copyright © 1980 by David A. Adler.

We have been unable to trace the copyright holder in the story 'Mrs Simkin's Bathtub' by Linda Allen from pp.48-52 *The New Golden Land Anthology* (Penguin) and would appreciate any information that would enable us to do so.

We are grateful to the following for permission to reproduce photographs: Barnaby's Picture Library pp.46 above centre (photo: Bill Meadows), 46 below left, 47 below left; Camera Press pp.47 above left (photo: Ian Cuthbertson), 47 centre right (photo: Chris Hewitt); J. Allan Cash pp.46 above right, 46 below right, 46 above left, 47 above centre, 47 above right; Michael Holford p.47 below right; The Hutchinson Library p.47 below centre; Northern Ireland Tourist Board p.47 centre left; Northern Picture Library p.46 below centre.

Illustrators, other than those acknowledged with each story, include: Val Biro pp.48-59; Brett Colquhoun pp.42-43; Lorraine Ellis p.40; Ian Heard pp.46-47; Sandra Laroche pp.44, 60-63; Carol McLean Carr pp.30-39; Lorraine Ellis pp.40-41; Geo Parkin p.64; Dave Parkins pp.4-12; Bryna Waldman pp.14-21; Chris Winn p.13.

No, only what
Brontosaur.

CONTENTS

Mrs Simkin's Bathtub

"Are you aware," said Mr Simkin to Mrs Simkin one morning, "that the bathtub's half-way down the stairs?"

"How very inconvenient," said Mrs Simkin, going to have a look. "How long has it been there?"

"I have no idea," said Mr Simkin. "It was in the bathroom when I went to bed last night, and now it's here, so it must have moved when we were asleep."

"Well, we shall just have to make the best of it," said Mrs Simkin, "Will you bath first or shall I?"

"I will," said Mr Simkin bravely.

He stepped into the bathtub. It wobbled a bit at first, but it soon settled down. Mrs Simkin fetched soap and towels, shampoo and bath salts, and arranged them nicely on the stairs.

"There," she said, "it doesn't look too bad now, and if I polish the taps and scrub the feet it should look quite smart. I'm sure none of the neighbours has a bathtub on the stairs."

Mr Simkin said she was probably right.

After a day or two they hardly noticed that the bathtub was there at all. It didn't really inconvenience them to squeeze past it when they wanted to go upstairs, and the landing smelt so pleasantly of bath oil that Mrs Simkin began to feel quite happy about it.

She invited the lady next door to have a look, but the lady next door said that she didn't approve of these modern ideas and, anyhow, she had never been one to give herself airs.

One morning Mr Simkin went to have his bath. "My dear!" he cried. "Come and see! The bathtub's gone!"

"Gone!" cried Mrs Simkin, leaping out of bed. "Gone where?"

"I don't know," said Mr Simkin, "but it isn't on the stairs."

"Perhaps it's back in the bathroom," said Mrs Simkin. They went to have a look but it wasn't there.

"We shall have to buy another one," said Mr Simkin as they went down to breakfast. The bathtub was in the kitchen.

"You know, my dear," said Mr Simkin a few minutes later, "this is a much better place for a bathtub than half-way down the stairs. I quite like having breakfast in the bath."

"Yes," said Mrs Simkin, "I like it here, too. The bath towels match the saucepans, and think of all the soup I shall be able to make when we have a large dinner-party."

"That's a very good point," agreed Mr Simkin, "I can't think why everybody doesn't want a bathtub in their kitchen."

One day Mr and Mrs Simkin went downstairs to find that the bathtub had moved again. It was in the living-room, sitting snugly before the fire.

"Oh, I don't think I like it there," said Mrs Simkin, looking at it with her head on one side.

"Neither do I," said Mr Simkin, "although it will be very pleasant bathing in front of the fire."

"I don't suppose it will stay there very long," whispered Mrs Simkin. "Once a bathtub has started to roam, it never knows when to stop."

7

She was quite right. The following morning the bathtub was underneath the sideboard, which was rather difficult for bathing, but they managed somehow. Two or three days later they found the bathtub in the basement with spiders in it.

On the day that Mrs Simkin was forty-two years old they couldn't find the bathtub anywhere.

"What shall I do?" cried Mrs Simkin, "I wanted to use that lovely bubble bath that you gave me for my birthday."

"So did I," said Mr Simkin.

The lady next door came round.

"Happy birthday," she said. "Did you know that your bathtub was on the front lawn?"

They all went to have a look.

There was a horse drinking out of it.

"Go away," said Mrs Simkin to the horse. "How dare you drink my bathwater, you greedy creature?" and she stepped recklessly into the bathtub.

The lady next door said she didn't know what the world was coming to and she went home and locked herself indoors.

As the bubbles floated down the street, lots of people came to see what was going on. They saw Mrs Simkin sitting in the bathtub. They were very interested. They leaned on the fence and watched. They asked if they could come again.

As the days went by, Mrs Simkin began to think that the bathtub would stay on the front lawn for ever, but one morning when there was rather a chilly wind about they found the bathtub in the greenhouse. The people in the street were very disappointed. They got up a petition asking Mr Simkin to bring it back.

"My dear," said Mr Simkin a few days later, "do you happen to know where the bathtub is today?"

"No, Stanley," said Mrs Simkin, "but today's Tuesday. It's quite often in the garage on Tuesdays."

"It isn't there today," said Mr Simkin.

"Have you tried the verandah?" suggested Mrs Simkin. "It hasn't been there for some time."

"I've looked everywhere," said Mr Simkin, "It isn't in the house and it isn't in the garden."

10

Mrs Simkin was busy with something else. "I do hope it hasn't gone next door," she sighed. "The lady next door has no sympathy with that kind of thing."

Mr Simkin went to inquire. "The lady next door said that she wouldn't allow anyone else's bathtub in her house, and that she was of the opinion that people ought to be able to control their bathtubs." Mr Simkin went home.

Mr Robinson from across the street rang up. "I know it's none of my business," he said, "but I thought you'd like to know that your bathtub's sitting up on the roof of your house."

Mrs Simkin thanked him for the information. Mr Simkin went to take his bath. He said there was a marvellous view from up there. Mrs Simkin climbed up. All the people cheered. She thought it was rather nice, but she had no head for heights. Perhaps it was time to ring the plumber.

The plumber said that wandering bathtubs weren't really in his line of business and why didn't they get in touch with the Department of the Environment?

Mrs Simkin said she wasn't going to all that trouble. She would soon get used to bathing on the roof. So they left the bathtub where it was. And that's where it liked to be best of all.

The people in the street had a meeting in Mr Simkin's greenhouse. They decided to have their bathtubs on their roofs as well. All except the lady next door. She preferred to take a shower.

Written by Linda Allen,
illustrated by Dave Parkins

Fork Week

You're going to lay the table.
You go to the drawer to get the knives, forks and
spoons.
You find the forks
You find the spoons
but the knives – they've all gone.
You look everywhere
the sink, the table, the draining board
but they've all gone.

A few days later – it's the same
only it's the spoons this time
and all the knives have come back.

My brother,
he's worked it out,
he says they take it in turns to disappear.
"It's alright," he says,
"We won't see another fork till Thursday,
it's Fork Week."

Michael Rosen

When Connor Lost His Cows

Young Farmer Connor once lost two of his best cows.
Nobody knew where they had gone. He asked at every
house in the village, but nobody had seen them. So
he took his big walking-stick and set off to look for
them. He walked for miles and miles, but could find
no trace of them.

When night began to fall, he was hungry and tired
and there was no place to rest for the night because he
had walked and walked miles away from the village
and ended up in the middle of a wild heath.

He was just about to lie down in the heather, when he suddenly saw a light. Was it coming from a house? He decided to go and see. As he came closer, he saw that the light was coming from a small window in an old hut.

What should he do? Perhaps some wild robbers lived there? Well, he decided to take a chance and knocked on the door. It opened straightaway and an old man with very dark eyes stood there.

"Come in," he said. "You're very welcome. We've been waiting for you."

So young Farmer Connor went in, gripping his stick very tight in case of danger.

"Meet my wife!" said the old man and Connor saw
an old woman sitting at the table, making a meal. She
had long sharp teeth and bright green eyes. "Sit
yourself down and make yourself at home," she said
with a smile.

So Connor sat down and rested his hot feet and
aching legs, while the old woman went to stir the big
pot on the fire. And all the time, Connor felt that she
was keeping an eye on him.

Then suddenly there came a knock on the door.
The old man went and opened it and in walked a
fine young black wolf. It walked straight through the
living room and disappeared into another room.
Then, in the twinkling of an eye, a handsome young
man came out of the same room and sat down at
the table.

"You are welcome here," he said to Connor.
"We've been waiting for you." But before Connor
could say Jack Robinson, there was another knock on
the door. And again a young wolf came in and again
it went straight into the other room. Again a
handsome young man came out to the living room.
And he also sat down at the table.

Then the old woman served the meal and the old
man said, "These two fine young men are our sons.
You must tell them why you've come here and what
you want. We all keep to ourselves and we don't like
strangers poking into our affairs and spying on us."

So Connor told them about how he'd lost his two cows and of how he had searched all day long for them. "I don't know where I am," he went on. "I've never been here before. I've not come to spy on you, so if you can give me any idea about how to find my cows, I'll get out from under your feet and go on my way."

Then the old couple and their sons all laughed and Connor saw the firelight gleam on the long sharp teeth of the old woman. And suddenly, angry and frightened, he leaped out of his chair and grabbed his heavy walking-stick. Then he shouted at them. "Don't laugh at me! Just open the door and I'll be off. Then you can laugh on the other side of your faces and good riddance!"

But the older brother held out his hand in friendship and said, "Wait. There's no need to be angry. Do you remember how one day you found a young wolf with a thorn in its foot? How you saw it limping? And how you pulled that thorn out of its foot?"

"Indeed I do!" said Connor. "The poor beast was so pleased, he licked my hand!"

"Well, now," said the young man, "I am the very same wolf that licked your hand. And I've never forgotten your kindness. So sit down, and finish your food, then stay with us for the night. And have no fear."

So Connor sat down and they all fed their faces and joked and laughed. And when they were full, they all fell asleep.

Next morning, Connor woke up and rubbed his eyes. He was lying on top of a haystack in his very own farmyard.

"What a foolish dream I had last night," he muttered to himself. "What a silly dream!"

Then he stretched and got up. Then he thought, "Well, if it wasn't a silly dream, then my cows will have come back!"

So he rushed to the cow-shed, but there was no sign of his two lost cows. "Perhaps they're in the big field," he thought, not really believing it. So he rushed out to the field.

And in the field he didn't find his two lost cows, but he did find three new cows that were the finest he'd ever seen.

"Oh, they must have strayed out of the neighbour's field," he said. So he took his big stick and went to drive them out of his field. But when the cows reached the gate, a young wolf rushed out from behind the wall and snapped at the cows' feet and drove them back into Connor's field.

And Connor said to the wolf, "Well, I'll not quarrel with you today! And if ever you get another thorn in your foot, you know where to come!" Then he scratched his head and laughed. "If the neighbours catch me talking to a wolf, they'll think I'm crazy!"

And the young wolf smiled a big wide smile and disappeared into the woods.

Written by Geoffrey Summerfield,
illustrated by Bryna Waldman

CAM JANSEN

and the Mystery of the Missing Bones

Cam Jansen's real name is Jennifer, but when people found out about her amazing memory they started calling her "The Camera" — "Cam" for short. When Cam and her friend Eric are at the museum, Cam is the only one to notice that some bones are missing from the dinosaur display. The two children are looking for clues when they see a milkman acting suspiciously. They jump on their bicycles and follow him to a house . . .

There was a high window on the side of the garage. As Cam walked past the window, she heard voices. She looked for something to stand on so that she could look inside.

Someone tapped her on the back. It was Eric.

"I locked the bicycles to the fence," he said. "I didn't want to wait out there alone."

Cam found an empty wooden milk crate behind the house. She put the crate right under the window, climbed up, and looked through.

There was a large table inside the garage. A few small bones and some larger ones were on the table. The milk crate with the brown bag that they had seen the man put in the truck was there, too. A bag of plaster of Paris was on the floor near some boxes, and metal tubs and a wheelbarrow with a pickaxe and shovel in it.

23

"Get down," Eric whispered. "Someone will see you."

"There's no one there," Cam said. "But there is an open door. Maybe it leads into the house. I'll bet that's where they went."

Eric climbed onto the crate.

"Look!" Eric said. "The three missing bones are on that table!"

Eric got off the crate. He pulled on Cam's sleeve. "Get down," he said. "Let's go back now."

Cam didn't move. She kept looking through the window.

"We can call the museum," Eric said. "We can tell them we found their missing dinosaur bones."

"Someone is coming through the door," Cam said. "It's the milkman."

Eric quickly climbed onto the crate. Cam and Eric watched the milkman take the brown bag out of the crate. The bag was tied with string. The milkman tried to untie the knot. He couldn't.

"Why did you tie it so tightly?" he called into the house.

"Use the scissors," a woman's voice answered.

The milkman reached into one of the boxes. He took out a pair of scissors and cut the string.

"I wonder what's in there?" Eric whispered.

"It can't be a bone from the Coelophysis," Cam said quietly. "It's too big."

The milkman tore open the side of the bag. There was something large and white inside. He took it out and carefully placed it on the table.

"Wow!" Eric said. "Look at the size of that bone."

"It must be from the Brachiosaurus," Cam said, "the one they were mending in the museum."

The milkman took out a ruler and measured the bone. He took a pad and pencil from his pocket and wrote on the pad. Then he looked at the bag of plaster of Paris.

"We need more plaster," he called into the house.

"Then let's go and get it," the woman answered.

The milkman walked through the open door and into the house.

"They'll probably use the plaster of Paris to make a copy of the bone," Cam said. "They'll take the copy to the museum tomorrow and leave it there in place of the real one."

"But how do they get in and out of the museum?" Eric asked.

"And why do they want the bones?" Cam added.

Cam and Eric stopped talking. They heard the front door of the house open and then slam shut.

After a few minutes Cam whispered, "I didn't hear the truck drive away, but they should have gone by now. Let's take a look."

Cam walked quietly. Eric followed her. Cam peeked out past the edge of the garage wall. She saw that the truck was still in the driveway. And she saw something else.

"Our bicycles," Cam said. "What if *they* see them!"

"We *did* see your bicycles," a man said.

Cam turned. It was the milkman. He was standing behind Eric.

by *David A. Adler*, illustrated by *David Pearson*

Mysterious monsters of the past

Dinosaurs roamed most of the world for over a hundred million years. They lived in nearly every country —even Britain.

Dinah Sorr,
Natural History Museum
London SW7 5BD

30

Q

Did you know that every single dinosaur died before there were any human beings?

No one ever saw them.
Or hunted them.
Or got eaten by them.
Or drew them on cave walls.

So, how do we know
what they looked like?
Ah, that's where
the detective
work begins.

By studying
their bones!

For a long time now, scientists have been digging up
bits of dinosaurs that have turned to stone — bones, teeth
and sometimes even dinosaur eggs. (These are called *fossils*.)

Even the dinosaurs' footprints in the mud have turned to
stone in some places, so the scientists can work out how
big and heavy the creatures were.

Using the fossils as clues, they have fitted all the bits
together to give some idea of what the dinosaurs looked
like. (It's like working on an enormous jigsaw when most of
the pieces are missing!)

How can scientists know what dinosaurs ate?

The teeth are the clues.

Meat-eaters needed strong, sharp teeth for tearing and cutting.

But plant-eaters' teeth were short and blunt, so they could grind and mash their food.

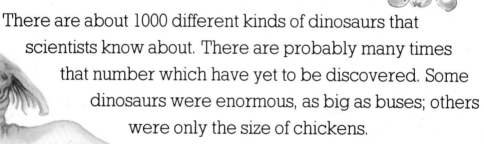

There are about 1000 different kinds of dinosaurs that scientists know about. There are probably many times that number which have yet to be discovered. Some dinosaurs were enormous, as big as buses; others were only the size of chickens.

Some walked on four legs, others on their two hind legs.

Some had bumps, some had horns, some had spikes and some even wore great bony plates like suits of armour.

BUT — in one way the dinosaurs were all alike. They were a kind of *reptile* — like the lizards and crocodiles we know today.

And that explains the name: dino — means terrible

saurus — means lizard.

What was the world of the dinosaurs like?

It was a world of great seas, huge lakes and, in some places, enormous, flat, muddy swamps.

It was much hotter too, with no cold seasons. It was even warm at the South and North Pole.

Warm and wet — the right climate for dinosaurs!

When did these strange animals live?

Here's a chart to help you work it out.

230 million years ago	**Early Triassic period** No dinosaurs yet.	
200 million years ago	**Late Triassic period** The first dinosaurs appear. They are probably all small and meat-eaters, but by the end of the period some very big ones have appeared. There is also a giant plant-eater around. Coelophysis lives now.	Lasted 35 million years.
195 million years ago	**Jurassic period** More kinds of dinosaurs about, especially plant-eating ones. Some of these are simply enormous. Many walked on their hind legs so they could feed on the tops of trees. The dinosaurs who used four legs often had flat plates growing up from the skin on their backs. Brachiosaurus lives now.	Lasted 55 million years.
140 million years ago	**Cretaceous period** The world is full of dinosaurs. Most of the giant plant-eaters have died out, but there are lots of new, smaller ones. Tyrannosaurus Rex, biggest meat-eater ever, lives now, but so do many of the trees we know. And for the first time there are flowers.	Lasted 75 million years.
65 million years ago	The dinosaurs have gone. No humans yet.	
2 million years ago Today	Human beings appear.	

Mesozoic Era

Cenozoic Era

The dinosaurs
CAM JANSEN knew about

Coelophysis

Coelophysis lived in the Triassic period, a time when the land was becoming drier and there were more plains and jungles than there had been before. There were still lots of swamps and lakes and seas, but a few volcanoes had popped up.

Length: around 3 metres.

Weight: about the same weight as you. (Its bones were hollow, like a bird's.)

Teeth: sharp, with rough edges like a saw. (So we know it was a meat-eater.)

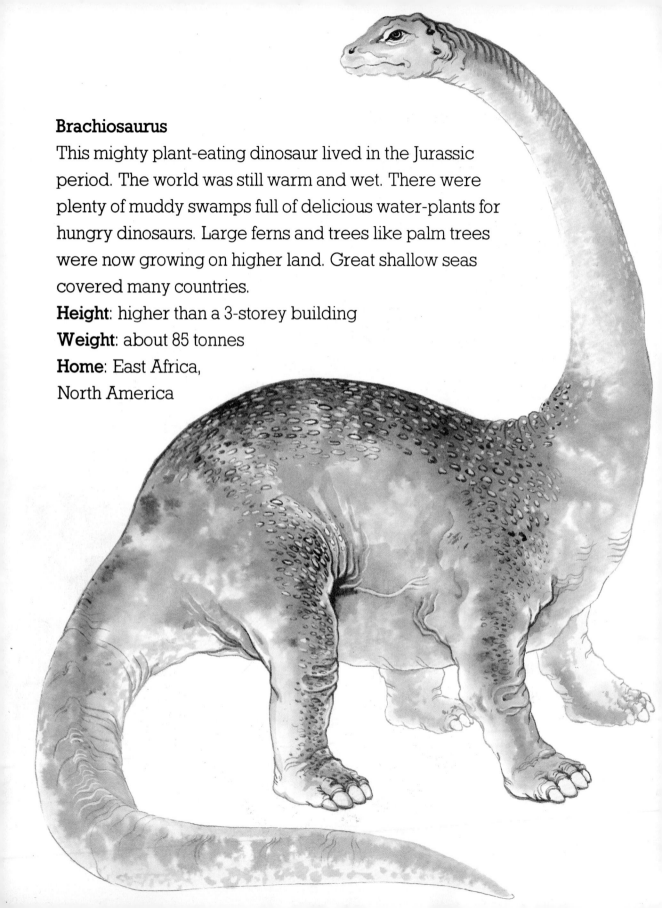

Brachiosaurus

This mighty plant-eating dinosaur lived in the Jurassic period. The world was still warm and wet. There were plenty of muddy swamps full of delicious water-plants for hungry dinosaurs. Large ferns and trees like palm trees were now growing on higher land. Great shallow seas covered many countries.

Height: higher than a 3-storey building

Weight: about 85 tonnes

Home: East Africa,
North America

Dino definitions

What do the names mean?

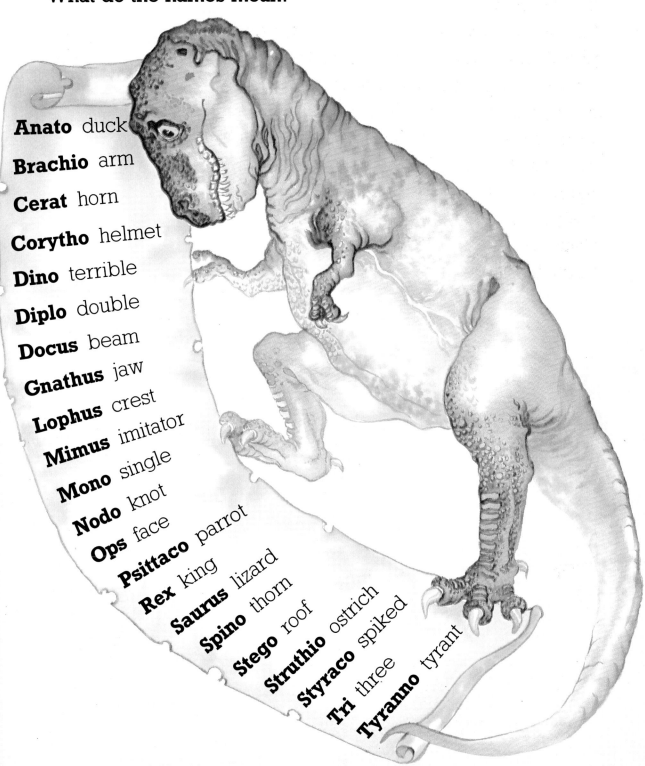

Anato duck

Brachio arm

Cerat horn

Corytho helmet

Dino terrible

Diplo double

Docus beam

Gnathus jaw

Lophus crest

Mimus imitator

Mono single

Nodo knot

Ops face

Psittaco parrot

Rex king

Saurus lizard

Spino thorn

Stego roof

Struthio ostrich

Styraco spiked

Tri three

Tyranno tyrant

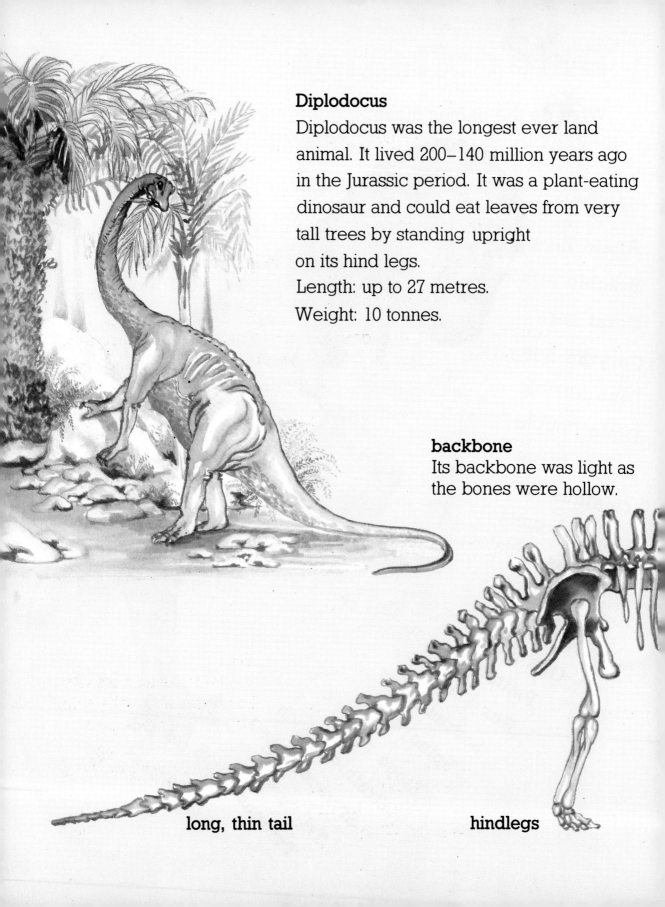

Diplodocus

Diplodocus was the longest ever land animal. It lived 200–140 million years ago in the Jurassic period. It was a plant-eating dinosaur and could eat leaves from very tall trees by standing upright on its hind legs.

Length: up to 27 metres.

Weight: 10 tonnes.

backbone

Its backbone was light as the bones were hollow.

long, thin tail   **hindlegs**

Mysteries still to solve

? How long did a dinosaur live?

? What kind of noise did a dinosaur make?

? Were all dinosaurs born from eggs?

? Why did the dinosaurs die out?

Who knows . . . one day you might become a scientist and help find the answers.

long, thin neck

skull
Its skull was tiny, and its brain was about the same size as that of a kitten.

thick body

forelegs
Its leg and thigh bones were large and heavy to support its great weight.

39

MAKE YOUR OWN

What you need:

One egg carton

Several cardboard rolls, like the ones you find in waxed or grease proof paper

One piece of cardboard, shaped like this ...
then rolled up into a cone like this

Plenty of Sellotape and masking tape.

Paint and paint brushes, or a can of spray paint and markers.

Use the picture as a guide to make your dinosaur.

DINOSAUR

Cut 2 egg containers from the carton. Use one for top of head and the other as a snout.

Cut rolls to any size you like and join with tape.

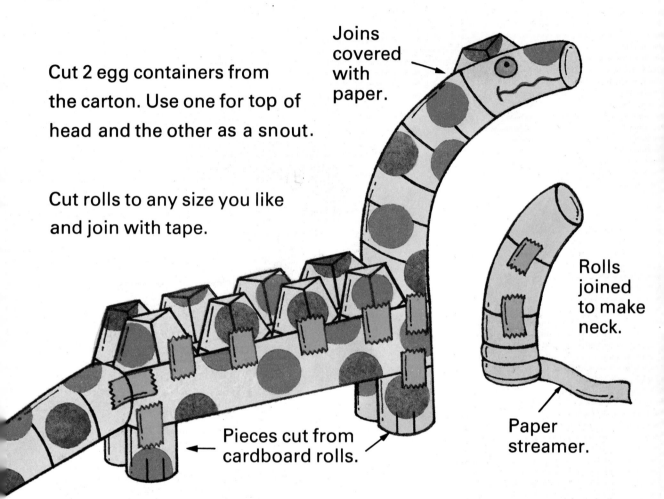

Joins covered with paper.

Rolls joined to make neck.

Pieces cut from cardboard rolls.

Paper streamer.

Cut streamers from paper and wind these around neck and tail to cover joins.

Paint your dinosaur and mark in eyes, mouth and claws.

Now give your new pet a name. How about Dorothea or Douglas? Or add "saurus" to your own name: Dorotheasaurus or Douglasaurus!

HERE, BOY!

The Teradactyls have all gone,
the Dinosaurs are dead —
except for one small sleepy chap
that hides beneath my bed.
I know he's breathing fire and smok
although there's none to see,
I wish he'd shake himself awake
and come and speak to me.
I think HE thinks that he's a dog
or 'praps' a largish cat.
I KNOW he is a DINOSAUR
　　so let's not argue that!

Peg Dunstan

SO BIG!

The dinosaur, an ancient beast,
I'm told, was very large.
His eyes were big as billiard balls,
His stomach, a garage.
He had a huge and humping back,
A neck as long as Friday.
I'm glad he lived so long ago
And didn't live in my day!

Max Fatchen

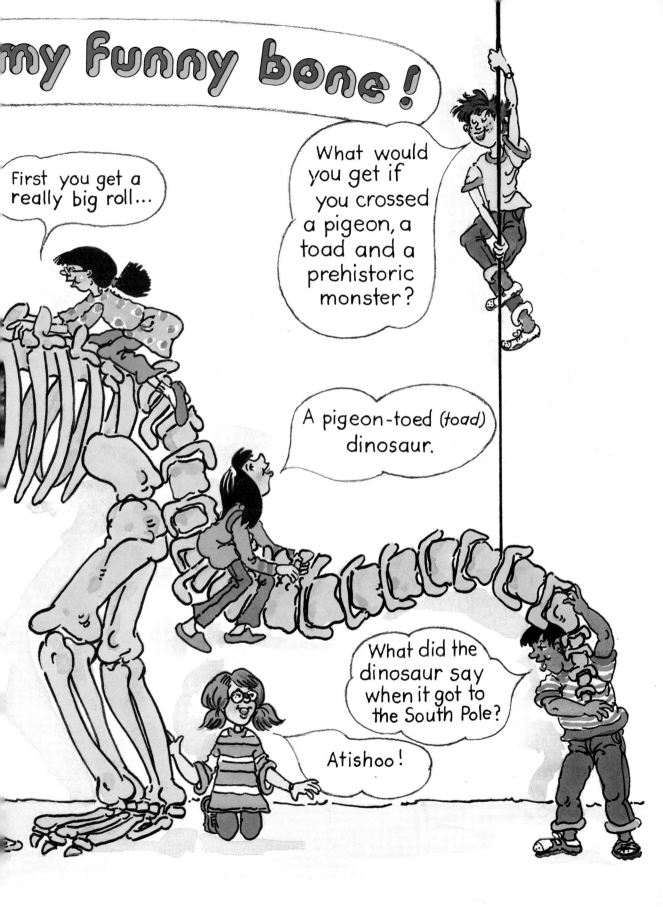

Landmarks of the British Isles

Ben Nevis, in Scotland, is the highest mountain in the British Isles, at a height of 1,392 metres above sea level.

Shetland

There are more than two hundred islands making up the **British Isles**. The **mainland**, that is Scotland, England and Wales together, is the eighth largest island in the world.

Orkney

Hebrides

Lough Neagh, in Northern Ireland, is the largest natural lake in the British Isles.

The **Farne Islands**, off the Northumberland coast, are a nature reserve. Seals and many kinds of seabirds can be seen there.

Isle of Man

Windermere, in the Lake District, is the largest lake in England. It is over 16 kilometres long.

Isles of Scilly

Channel Islands

The **River Shannon**, in the Republic of Ireland, is the longest river in the British Isles. It is 370 kilometres long.

Snowdon is the highest mountain in Wales. It is 1,085 metres high.

The biggest **waterwheel** in the world is in the Isle of Man, and is called *The Lady Isabella*.

Inverness is one of the oldest towns in Scotland. It is situated on the River Ness, and is often called the capital of the Highlands.

Stirling Castle stands high on a hillside looking down on the River Forth. It is one of Scotland's royal palaces, and Mary, Queen of Scots was Crowned there, as an infant.

Londonderry has the only unbroken walls around any city in the British Isles.

The **suspension bridge**, across the River Humber at Hull, is the longest in Europe.

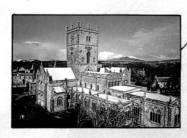

St David's is the smallest cathedral city in the British Isles.

Stonehenge, a prehistoric stone circle, was built over four thousand years ago, on Salisbury Plain.

The only **Roman lighthouse** still standing in the British Isles can be seen at Dover.

The Umbrella Mystery

A play

Rabbit
(whose umbrella
gets lost)

Badger
(who loves big
red umbrellas)

Squirrel
(who thinks of
the toaster)

Hedgehog
(who worries
about the TV)

Characters

Toad
(who likes
rain-bathing)

Magpie
(who has waterproof
feathers)

Scene: *Badger's gate. He is leaning on it and looking up at the sky. He sniffs.*

Badger   It smells like rain.
(*Rabbit comes in from the left. She is carrying a book.*)

Rabbit   Hello Badger.

Badger   Hello Rabbit. I wouldn't go out if I were you.
It smells like rain.

Rabbit   I know. But I have to take this book back to Hare.

Badger   Then you should have your umbrella.
You know how nasty wet fur feels.

Rabbit   But I can't find my umbrella.
I've looked and looked but I can't find it anywhere.

Badger   Oh my teeth and claws!
           Not your beautiful big red umbrella?
           Do you think a burglar came and stole it?

Rabbit   Oh, no. Burglars don't steal umbrellas.

Badger   If I was a burglar I would.
           I like umbrellas – especially big red ones.

Rabbit   I just wish I could remember where I put it.
           (*She sniffs.*)
           That rain smells closer. I'd better hurry.
           Goodbye Badger.
           (*She goes off to the right, muttering.*)
           It wasn't in the cupboard and it wasn't
           under the bed and it wasn't
           behind the door . . .

Badger   *(calling after her)* I'm sure a burglar took it!
(to himself) Oh my teeth and claws.
What a dreadful thing.
Poor Rabbit. Poor, poor Rabbit.

Squirrel comes in.

Squirrel   Hello Badger. It smells like rain doesn't it?

Badger   Oh, Squirrel, guess what!
A burglar must have taken Rabbit's umbrella.
You know, the beautiful big red umbrella that
she had for Christmas?

Squirrel   What's that? A burglar?
Ooo, you've made my nose go all twitchy.
What else did he take?

Badger   I don't know, she didn't say.

Squirrel   I bet he took her toaster.
It makes such beautiful toast too.

Badger   You're probably right. It *is* a lovely toaster.

51

Toad and Hedgehog come in.

Hedgehog Hello Badger, hello Squirrel.

Toad Have you noticed that it smells like rain?

Squirrel Oh Toad and Hedgehog, guess what!
A burglar stole Rabbit's
big red umbrella and her toaster.

Hedgehog It's enough to make your prickles curl.
Oh dear, 1 feel all funny.

Toad There, there, Hedgehog. Don't upset yourself.
(*He pats her on the back.*)
What else did he take?

Squirrel We don't know. She didn't say.

Hedgehog He probably took her new TV.
She only bought it last week.

Badger   That's right . . . and now it's gone!
We won't be able to see Bugs Bunny!

Hedgehog Or Daffy Duck!

Squirrel   Or Sylvester the cat . . . . I've never seen him in colour.

Toad   He's not coloured. He's black and white.

Magpie comes in.

Magpie   Hello everyone. I think it's going to rain.
My feathers feel sticky.

Toad   Oh Magpie, guess what!
A burglar got into Rabbit's house and
stole her big red umbrella . . .

Hedgehog . . . and her toaster . . .

Squirrel   . . . AND her TV!

Badger   That's right.

Magpie   What's that? A burglar? Oh my beak and wings!
Did you say the TV's gone?

All	Yes!
Magpie	And the toaster?
All	Yes!
Magpie	Whatever shall we do without them?
Badger	*(sadly)* He took her umbrella too.
Magpie	I don't mind about the umbrella. Magpies don't use them. Waterproof feathers, you know. But I *am* going to miss the toaster and the TV.
Squirrel	*(Holding out his hand.)* We'd better go. It's starting to rain.
Badger	*(Looking off to the right.)* Look! Look everyone! It's the burglar!
Squirrel	Where? Where?
Toad	I can't see a burglar.
Hedgehog	I feel all funny again.
Magpie	Where? Show me!

Badger   There! Walking along under Rabbit's big red umbrella.

Magpie   Quick, let's hide and then when he comes past we can jump out and catch him.

Squirrel   Good idea! Come on everyone, get down behind the gate.

Badger   Hurry up, here he comes.

They all get down behind the gate.

Squirrel   (*in a loud whisper*) When do we jump out?

Magpie   Ssh! When I say "Go!"

A big red umbrella comes on. We can't really see who is under it, but the feet look like Rabbit's!

Magpie   Ready . . . . steady . . . . . GO!

They all jump up and yell at once.

Magpie   Stick 'em up!

Squirrel   Freeze!

Badger   Hands up!

Toad   Don't move!

Hedgehog We've got you covered!

The umbrella is whisked away and Rabbit is revealed.

Rabbit   What's going on?

All   Rabbit! It's you!

Rabbit   Of course it's me. Who did you think it was?

All   The burglar who stole your umbrella!

Rabbit   What burglar? Who said my umbrella had been stolen?

Magpie   Toad told me, didn't you Toad?

Toad   Yes but Squirrel told Hedgehog and me, didn't he?

Hedgehog   That's right, he did.

Squirrel   Yes but Badger told me, didn't you Badger?

57

Badger   No . . . . er . . . . Yes . . . . er
(He looks very uncomfortable.)
I thought a burglar might have . . .
(He takes a deep breath.)
And then I told Squirrel that a burglar must have . . .
(His voice gets quieter and quieter.)
And that just seemed to make it all happen . . .
(He looks down at his feet.)

Rabbit   But nobody stole my umbrella. Hare had it.
I'd forgotten that I lent it to him when he came over
last week. It started to rain and he does hate to
get his fur wet. You *are* silly, Badger.

Squirrel   *(quickly)* I've just noticed that it's raining.
I must be off. Goodbye.

Hedgehog Me too. I haven't got time to stop and chat.
Bye everyone.

Toad   Yes, I'll be off too.
I fancy a spot of rain-bathing in the garden.

Magpie   I'll be going as well. Rain brings the worms out
you know and *I* fancy a nice worm pie.
Cheerio.

Rabbit	Come on Badger. Come under my umbrella and we'll go home and make some toast.
Badger	All oozing and dripping with butter?
Rabbit	Of course! Then we'll watch Bugs Bunny on TV.
Badger	I'd like that.
Rabbit	And then I'm going to lend you a book. I think you'll like that too!
Badger	What's it called?
Rabbit	"Badger's Best Blunder"!

By Pat Edwards, adapted by Wendy Body,
illustrated by Val Biro

ARE YOU A GOOD

Help! Robbery! Two well-known robbers, Bert and Daisy, have burgled this house. What have they stolen? Have they replaced anything? How many things have they moved or touched?

DETECTIVE ?

The picture on page 60 shows what the room looked like before the burglary; the picture on page 61 is the same room afterwards. Are you a good detective? You should be able to find at least 20 clues which tell you that the robbers have broken in.

WATCH FOR BURGLARS

BERT

GLUE

Who stole the secret papers?

"We know one of you stole the secret papers," said Sam Supersleuth to the two spies. "The question is: who?"

"I admit I did take them from your desk," said Artful Arthur, "but only because I knew Sally Sly was looking for them. I put them between pages 63 and 64 in that book you'll find in Sally's bag. If the papers aren't there, you'll know she has already handed them on."

"That's not true," gasped Sally. "Arthur gave me that book only an hour ago."

"A likely story," sneered Arthur, "she's lying."

"Oh no, she isn't," said Sam. "You're the one who's lying."

How did he know?

In any book, pages 63 and 64 are either side of the same leaf.

Find a word you don't know
Glossary

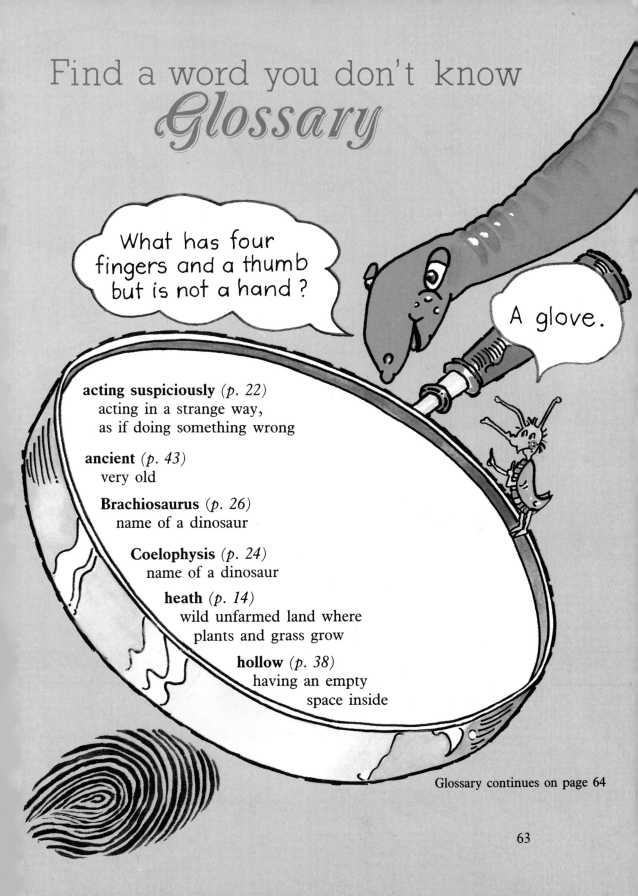

What has four fingers and a thumb but is not a hand ?

A glove.

acting suspiciously (*p. 22*)
    acting in a strange way,
    as if doing something wrong

ancient (*p. 43*)
    very old

Brachiosaurus (*p. 26*)
    name of a dinosaur

Coelophysis (*p. 24*)
    name of a dinosaur

heath (*p. 14*)
    wild unfarmed land where
    plants and grass grow

hollow (*p. 38*)
    having an empty
    space inside

Glossary continues on page 64

inconvenient *(p. 4)*
causing difficulty

peeked *(p. 29)*
peeped

petition *(p. 10)*
a letter sent by many people together,
asking for something

plaster of Paris *(p. 23)*
a paste that sets hard; used to make a mould for
making copies of something

"praps" *(p. 42)*
perhaps

recklessly *(p. 9)*
carelessly and dangerously

roamed *(p. 30)*
to wander about; ramble

Teradactyl *(p. 42)*
another way of spelling Pterodactyl, a dinosaur

verandah *(p. 10)*
a roofed area built onto a house, with no outside wall